712776

◆FOCUS◆
Reading for Success

Whistles and Dreams

PROGRAM AUTHORS
Richard L. Allington
Ronald L. Cramer
Patricia M. Cunningham
G. Yvonne Pérez
Constance Frazier Robinson
Robert J. Tierney

PROGRAM CONSULTANTS
Bernadine J. Bolden
Ann Hall
Sylvia M. Lee
Dolores Perez
Jo Ann Wong

CRITIC READERS
Shirley Duncan
Helen Johncock
Eunice Shepard
Joy Stewart

John C. Manning, *Instructional Consultant*

SCOTT, FORESMAN AND COMPANY
Editorial Offices: Glenview, Illinois

Regional Sales Offices: Palo Alto, California •
Tucker, Georgia • Glenview, Illinois •
Oakland, New Jersey • Dallas, Texas

ACKNOWLEDGMENTS

Text

"Skyscraper" from *Alligator Pie* by Dennis Lee. Copyright © 1974 by Dennis Lee. Reprinted by permission of Houghton Mifflin Company and Macmillan of Canada, a Division of Gage Publishing Limited.

"Homes" by Ilo Orleans. Reprinted by permission.

Adapted from *Who's in Rabbit's House?* by Verna Aardema, copyright © 1977 by Verna Aardema. Reprinted by permission of the publisher, Dial Books for Young Readers, A Division of E.P. Dutton, Inc. and The Bodley Head.

"Tricia's Fish" from *Girls Can Too!* by Lee Bennett Hopkins. Copyright © 1972 by Lee Bennett Hopkins. Reprinted by permission of Curtis Brown, Ltd.

"Fireman" from *City Sandwich* by Frank Asch. Copyright © 1978 by Frank Asch. By permission of Greenwillow Books (A Division of William Morrow & Company, Inc.)

Lilian Moore, "Walking," in *I Feel the Same Way*. Copyright © 1967 by Lilian Moore. Reprinted with the permission of Atheneum Publishers.

Adaptation of "Blackmail" from *The Jataka Tales* by Nancy DeRoin. Copyright © 1975 by Nancy DeRoin. Reprinted by permission of Houghton Mifflin Company.

Stories by Verna Aardema, Alan Vance Bickley, Carol Boyd, Kate Holland, Jeanette Leardi, Liane Onish, Pauline Peck, Sallie Runck, Nancy DeRoin, Mary Shuter, Suzanne Slater, Mary McCarroll White.

Photographs

Page 56: James A. Sugar/Black Star;   Page 62: Jim Harrison/Lightwave;   Page 63: Dan Morrill;   Page 79: Tom Stack/Tom Stack & Associates;   Page 80: ANIMALS ANIMALS/Oxford Scientific Films;   Page 81: Mark Newman/Tom Stack & Associates;   Page 109: Wendell Metzen;   Pages 110–111: John M. Hall

Artists

Allen, Elizabeth 131;   Altshuler, Frank 112–119;   Anderson, Bill and Judie 156–157, 207;   Beckes, Shirley 52–53, 130, 199–205, 215;   Bornholdt, Karen 206;   Brett, Jan 24–25, 27, 100, 163–165;   Brewster, Patience 180–181;   Brown, Marc 42–43;   Cunningham, David 54–62;   Frederick, Larry 18–19, 64–74, 88–89;   Geyer, Jackie 182–184, 186–189;   Helmer, Jean 76–79, 83;   Hockerman, Dennis 41, 166–178;   Lexa, Susan 32–33, 35;   Koch, Carl 7, 20–23;   Magnuson, Diana 36–40, 144–145;   McCord, Kathleen 192–196, 198;   Miles, Elizabeth 75;   Miyaki, Yoshi 30–31, 132–142;   Neill, Eileen Mueller 109, 219–224;   Nelson, Anita 44–47;   Ormai, Stella 208–214;   Peterson, William 190–191;   Povilaitis, David 84–87, 99;   Rabinowitz, Sandy 120–122, 126;   Rigie, Jane 179;   Sanford, John 101–107;   Scott, Jerry 154–155;   Suyeoka, George 146–147, 149–151, 153;   Tenz, Freya 143;   Tien 48–51;   Traub, Pat 90–98

Freelance Photographs

Ryan Roessler 10–13, 199–205

Cover Artist

Elizabeth Miles

ISBN 0-673-21009-X

Contents

People Who Help

Some People Help

Some people work on this block. They help people who live here. If a water pipe breaks, who might come to fix it? If your pet is sick, who can help?

The Animal Doctor

Who would you call for help if your cat cried and cried all morning or your puppy cut its paw?

A vet can help. A vet is a doctor who helps animals. Some vets work on farms. Some vets work at zoos. This is Dr. Fry. She is a vet who works in a city. She helps sick pets.

Dr. Fry works here. Let's see what the doctor does in one day.

First, the doctor sees Sally's dog Flip. Flip is hopping because his paw is sore. The vet puts something on the sore paw to make it better. Dr. Fry talks to Sally about keeping Flip's sore paw clean. If his paw is clean, it will get better fast.

Dr. Fry likes to talk about how to take good care of pets.

Next, the doctor sees a cat named Tiger. Tiger is in a cage. Dr. Fry keeps some cages for animals that are too sick to be at their own houses.

The doctor takes Tiger out of his cage so she can look at his fur. Tiger's fur is shiny now and he is eating more. Tiger is getting better. He will go to his own house today. Dr. Fry gives Tiger a hug.

Then Mark comes in with his bird in a shoe box. The box has little holes in the top.

Mark says, "Hello, doctor. I have brought Chirpy to see you. She will not eat, and she does not sing. I don't know what to do."

The vet looks at Chirpy and says, "Chirpy has a cold. Keep her warm and give her two of these drops once a day."

Mark puts Chirpy back in the box to keep warm.

Dr. Fry is happy. This was a good day for her and for all her animals.

Hugs for Mr. Hill

Mr. Hill's work is fixing pipes that break. He can fix the pipes in people's houses. People call Mr. Hill the pipe doctor. When a pipe breaks and people have no water, they call Mr. Hill.

When Mr. Hill goes to a house, the pets follow him around. He does not ask the pets to follow him, they just do. Some of the pets even like to hug Mr. Hill! His work is not easy.

One day Mr. Brown needed a new pipe. So he called Mr. Hill. Then, while Mr. Hill worked on the pipe, something nibbled on his back. It was Mr. Brown's snake, Nibbles.

"What is this snake doing?" asked Mr. Hill.

Mr. Brown said, "Nibbles only wants to give you a little snake hug. A hug is his way of saying hello."

"A hug from a snake! What a day!" said Mr. Hill.

Next, at Mrs. Cook's house, her two cats just sat and looked while Mr. Hill worked. But when water came out of one pipe, the cats got wet. They ran away fast. Then they cried and cried. Cats don't like their fur to get wet.

The cats came back just as Mr. Hill was about to go. Both cats put their paws around Mr. Hill. They both hugged Mr. Hill with little fur paws.

"First I get a snake hug, and now I get a hug from these cats. What a day!" said Mr. Hill.

All Mr. Hill wanted to do now was to go to his own house. But when he got to his house, Mr. Hill saw something at the door with brown fur.

Mr. Hill looked at the thing. Then he got out of his van, went up to the door, and gave the thing in brown fur a hug.

The thing in fur hugged back and asked, "How did you know me, Daddy?"

Mr. Hill said, "I know my own little girl, even when she is dressed in fur. I got many hugs today. But this is the only one that makes me happy."

Neighbors Help

This is a safe and happy street to live on. People who live on this street are good neighbors. They do many things for one another. One neighbor keeps the children safe as they walk to school.

Mr. Wolf's Surprise

Children at Oak School see a note.

Help pick a good neighbor. Put the name of a good neighbor you know on paper. Tell why you picked that neighbor. The one picked to be the good neighbor will get a prize from the school.

Linda, look at this note. I want to pick a good neighbor. But I don't know what makes a good neighbor. I need help.

I need help too. Maybe Mr. Wolf can help. Let's go to Vine Street and talk to him.

The next day, Kevin and Linda named
Mr. Wolf their good neighbor. It was no
surprise that many of the children named
him too. One girl said Mr. Wolf helped
her learn how to skip. One boy said
Mr. Wolf made their street safe.

The Welcome Note

Yoshi did not like moving to a new street. On her old street a cat next door had just surprised her by having kittens. Yoshi was going to get one of the kittens, but she moved. Now she did not have a kitten.

Yoshi saw a note as she skated down the street. The note was tacked to a tree so people would see it. Yoshi read the note.

Lost
fluffy white cat

Reward for finding her. If you find her, take her to
123 Pine Street for the reward.

Mrs. Hope

After Yoshi read the note, she skated around the block. She saw a street sign with <u>Pine</u> on it, and she knew <u>Pine</u> was the name of the street in the note. Yoshi saw a green house with the number 123 on it. She knew that 123 was the number of Mrs. Hope's house.

Yoshi wanted to find out more about the cat and the reward in the note, so she skated up to the house to ask.

Mrs. Hope welcomed Yoshi, and Yoshi said, "I read your note. Did you find your cat yet? Did you give the reward?"

"Not yet. Why don't you look for Fluffy? Maybe you will find her and get the reward," said Mrs. Hope.

So Yoshi went down the street. She came to a tree. Near the tree was a little house. Yoshi looked in the door and saw a white cat, just like the one in Mrs. Hope's note. She was surprised to see kittens too.

Yoshi skated back and called, "Mrs. Hope! Come see Fluffy. She is in a safe place, and she has kittens!"

When Mrs. Hope looked into the little house, she said, "How wonderful! Thank you for finding her, Yoshi."

"You are welcome. Maybe I can help you with Fluffy's kittens," said Yoshi.

"Yes, you can. And you get the reward. It is a book about cats. Would you also like a kitten? When it is safe to take the kittens from Fluffy, you can have the one you want," said Mrs. Hope.

As she skated back to her house, Yoshi liked her new street much better.

Do you have neighbors who help you? You can make a book about people who help you.

1. First write about the people who help you. Tell what they do to help you.

2. Show in pictures something they do.

3. Put your writing and pictures together to make a book.

4. Make your book look pretty.

5. Put holes in your paper.

6. Put your book together with rings or with ribbons.

Now you can read your own book.

Everybody Helps

The people who live in these houses are busy. What are they doing? Do you see things you might do to help?

Ryan's Plan

Ryan lived in a house with his father, mother, and his little brother, Matt. The brothers had one bedroom.

Ryan did not enjoy a messy bedroom. He liked a clean bedroom better. So he always put his toys away.

Matt did not put his toys away. His side of the room was always messy. He enjoyed it that way.

At times their father said to Ryan, "Matt's side of the bedroom is messy. Yours is so much cleaner. Please help your brother pick up his toys."

Ryan liked the bedroom cleaner than Matt did. But Ryan did not like picking up his own toys and Matt's toys too.

Ryan needed to find a way to get Matt to pick up his own toys. Matt liked magic tricks. So Ryan planned to show Matt that picking up toys was a magic trick.

The next day, just before bedtime, Ryan started his plan by telling Matt about Magic Cleaner. He said Magic Cleaner did magic to pick up toys fast.

Matt said he wanted to do true magic just like Magic Cleaner.

Just before Matt went to sleep, he saw something. The thing seemed to float. Matt sat up to see better.

The thing said, "My name is Magic Cleaner. I enjoy cleaning. You can be a magic cleaner too. This ring is yours. It's magic. When you put it on, zap! You will be a magic cleaner. In the morning you will enjoy cleaning."

The next morning when Matt woke up, he looked at the magic ring. He saw the messy room and got busy. Matt made his bed and picked up toys. He made the magic come true. Then he called Ryan.

Ryan woke up and said, "You put away all your toys and some of mine too. Your side of the room is cleaner than mine. How did it get so clean?"

Matt showed Ryan his ring and said, "I just woke up and made the magic come true. I cleaned the room, and I enjoyed doing it. I am a magic cleaner."

A Day Too Hot for Penguins

"It's too hot today for a penguin.
I can not go out and play. What will I
do all day?" asked Penrod.

Penrod's mother said, "This morning
while I am at work, you are going to
Grandma and Grandpa's house. You know
they always have things to keep you
busy, even if it is hot."

When it was time to go, Penrod walked
to Grandma and Grandpa's house.

Penrod went into the house and said to Grandma, "Hello. I am here. I want to go out to play. But it's too hot!"

Grandma said, "It's very hot, Penrod. Grandpa is busy out in his truck. He is working on something you will enjoy. Why don't you go see what it is."

Penrod gave Grandma a big hug. Then he raced out to find Grandpa.

Grandpa was in his truck, just as Grandma said he would be. But Penrod was surprised to see what he was doing. Grandpa was busy sawing big blocks of clear ice into many little blocks.

"Hello, Grandpa. Grandma said you are working on something I will enjoy. Is all this ice for me?" asked Penrod.

"These cold blocks of ice are all
yours, my little penguin. Today is a
good day to make things from ice. And
if you keep the ice in the truck it will
last all day," said Grandpa.

"But, Grandpa, I don't know how to
make things from ice," said Penrod.

"You will see how easy it is, Penrod.
Just picture the toys you enjoy when
it's not so hot. Then get busy and make
the toys out of ice," said Grandpa.

Grandpa went away and Penrod got busy. The little penguin made many things from the ice.

Penrod enjoyed sliding, so he made a slide out of ice.

Penrod enjoyed playing in his wagon. So he made a fine ice wagon.

Penrod did not have a horse, but he wanted one. So he made one to ride.

Mother came to Grandma and Grandpa's house after work and called for Penrod to come in. But he was still busy, so he asked her to come out.

Mother went out. She was surprised to see all the toys Penrod had made from ice. She called to Grandma and Grandpa.

Grandpa and Grandma went out, and then Penrod said, "I made these toys for all of us. Will you play with me?"

They did. The whole penguin family played on Penrod's ice toys. It was not too hot a day for penguins after all.

A Perfect View

From the Top

The view from a tall building is best near the top. This city has some tall buildings. Which building might have the best view?

A View Best for Two

Mindy Mouse lived behind a set of plant pots on top of a tall building. The building was in a city that had many hills. So Mindy had a view of these hills from her building.

Mindy said the view was the best in the city. But she had no one to enjoy it with her.

Day after day Mindy said, "Who's going to come up and enjoy the best view in the city with me? Who's going to be my neighbor?"

A rain spout and a set of big steps
ran down the side of Mindy's building.
One day Mindy started down the steps.
She saw a cat with big paws.

The cat looked right at Mindy and
said, "Here is my lunch!"

Mindy was scared, but she saw the
rain spout. She jumped over the cat and
into the spout. The cat walked away.

The spout led right to the street, so
Mindy was soon safe and happy.
Then she met a turtle.

Mindy said, "Hello, Turtle. Would you like to come up to the top of this building to see the best view in the city? You will like looking out over the hills. You will like the view."

Turtle said, "Yes, I might like the view. But look at me. Who's going to help me go up these big steps?"

Mindy said, "You are little. But I'll help you get up to my house. I will go to the top and drop a rope down the spout. All you have to do is catch the rope and hold on. Then I'll pull you up."

Mindy ran up the steps to the top of the building. She dropped a rope down the spout. Turtle got it and pulled to let Mindy know she was set. Then Mindy pulled and pulled. She pulled Turtle right up the spout.

Turtle looked out over the hills and said, "It's a wonderful view. You are right. I wish I could live here, because it's the best view in the city."

Mindy said, "Turtle, you can."

From that day on the mouse and the turtle were neighbors. They looked out over the hills of the city together.

The New Game

"Are you set to play I Spy?" Kim
asked her sister, May.

Kim was by the window all set to play.
Kim could see a wonderful view of
the city because the Chens lived near the
top of a tall building. It was the
best place to play I Spy. But May was
still pushing her toy car over a hill
she made with a set of blocks. After
the car came down the hill, May put it
away and went over to the window.

"Now I can play. I'll go first.
I spy something red," said May.

Before Kim could say, "I spy," her
mother came in and said, "You know we
are going to eat at the Drakes' house on
the first floor. If you are dressed, you
can play for a while before we go."

May said, "Yes, we are dressed."

Kim said, "May, could the red thing
be a man's coat?"

Before May could say, "No," all the
lights went out.

Their father said, "All the lights
are out! I wonder what is going on? I
wonder if the Drakes still want us to
come to eat?"

Father called the Drakes, and the Drakes said they had candles and still wanted them to come. Mother, holding their only candle, led May, Kim, and father down the long set of steps. They still had many floors to go when the candle went out. They stopped because they could not see at all. They would just have to sit.

Then Kim said, "Since we can not play I Spy, I have a new game we can play. Let's play I Hear. I hear an animal noise."

May said, "It could be Sage, the new puppy on the floor over us."

Kim said, "You are right!"

May said, "Now it's my turn. I hear laughing."

Kim said, "I'll bet it's Jenny laughing."

Their mother and father had turns too. Then the lights came on. They went to the Drakes' house.

May said, "We can play I Hear even with the lights on. I bet the Drakes will like this game." And they did.

You can have secret talks with a neighbor. John talks to Sally with a mirror. One light says: come over. Two lights say: Let's play. Some days John and Sally write secret notes. Do you know what John said? Write it on some paper. Can you write a secret note too?

A=1   F=6   K=11   P=16   U=21   Z=26
B=2   G=7   L=12   Q=17   V=22
C=3   H=8   M=13   R=18   W=23
D=4   I=9   N=14   S=19   X=24
E=5   J=10 O=15   T=20   Y=25

9   8,1,22,5   1,14,5,23   19,5,20
15,6   2,15,15,11,19   3,15,13,5
15,22,5,18   1,14,4   19,5,5

Skyscraper

by Dennis Lee

Skyscraper, skyscraper,
Scrape me some sky:
Tickle the sun
While the stars go by.
Tickle the stars
While the sun's climbing high,
Then skyscraper, skyscraper
Scrape me some sky.

On the Water

Many people enjoy the water. Some people like to see it all the time. These people live on boats. They can take off any time they like. Their floating house can carry them to places far away.

Living on the Water

Some people think living on water is better than living on land. The Carver family thinks a boat is the best place to live.

This boat looks like a house. It is where the Carvers live all year long. Their boat sits at a dock just two feet from land. They live near the city. Father and Mother work in the city. Liz and Peter go to school there too.

The family goes to the city to buy many of the things they eat. They also like to catch fish to eat. Liz's father can fish right off the side of the boat. Liz likes to help him.

All the rooms on the boat are quite small. The Carvers eat in the sitting room because the kitchen is too small for the whole family. The sitting room is also where the family plays, reads, and lives.

When the family lived in a house on land, Peter had a big, messy bedroom. Not any more. Peter is a little sad that he can not keep his room full of old toys. If his little bedroom was full of toys now there would be no room for him.

Even though Liz's room is quite small, she likes it. She would probably be sad to live on land. She likes the way the boat rocks her to sleep.

The Carver family likes its boat because they enjoy the warm days under the open sky. The Carvers can even go for a swim off the side of their boat.

The best treat of all is that the Carvers' house can move. So when school is out Mother and Father take time off from work. Then their floating house will carry them off to see new places.

One day Peter and Liz saw Mother and Father looking at new maps. Peter and Liz knew a wonderful trip must be coming up.

A Trip on the Waterway

The children's last day of school came. Mother and Father said they were going on a long trip on the waterway.

Peter asked, "What is the waterway?"

Father opened the map and said to him, "Peter, the **waterway** is like a long street of water. There is land on both sides of the water. The water is gentle there so a trip on the waterway is quite safe. There is also much to see."

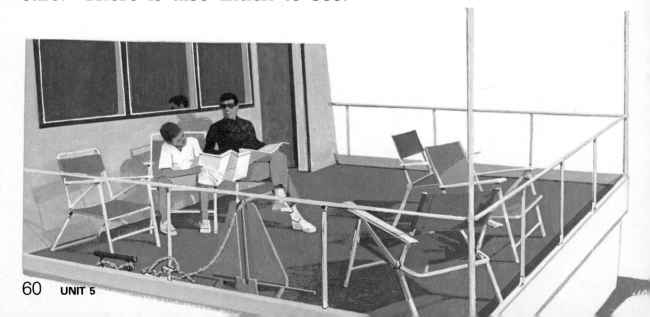

The Carvers left the next morning. They did not go too far in one day, because they liked to stop and see new places. They liked talking to new people they met too. In the heat of the day the Carvers stopped to swim off the side of their boat.

The waterway was full of ducks. Peter fed some of them. Then the ducks followed two feet behind the boat for a long time. Peter liked that.

Along the waterway they saw farm animals on land. Some days they saw steep hills and trees with red blossoms.

People who live on the land along the waterway have many fairs. The Carvers went to one. There was music to hear. There were old houses open for people to view. Some people were dressed in costumes from long ago. They cooked meat over an open fire.

Probably the best treat of the fair was a parade of boats. Old boats and new boats came down the waterway. The Carvers sat on their boat. Their seats were just six feet from the parade.

The whole trip up the waterway and back was full of treats and surprises. Liz and Peter were quite sad when their trip was over.

They knew there would probably be more trips. They knew their floating house would carry them to new places. But for years to come, they would think about the days they had on the waterway.

A Mountain Ranch

Some people live quite far from neighbors. They can talk to their neighbors on a radio. In the winter when the snow is deep an airplane can drop things people need. An airplane can also take people to a doctor.

The Sheep Ranch

The Vega family lives on a sheep ranch. On a sheep ranch, some things are the same year after year. In the spring the animals must be moved up the mountain to have more to eat. The water there is clear and good to drink. In the late fall the sheep are brought back to the ranch. Through the winter the sheep live in sheds that are warm and clean.

The sheep on a ranch have little to do but eat, sleep, and grow thick coats. But for the people who live on the ranch there is always work to be done.

Rita Vega and her little brother Tom like to sweep the barn and help with the animals. But the rule is that they must go to school too. Another rule is that school comes first. When school work is done, they learn about the ranch.

Rita and Tom learn about how to keep sheep safe. They learn how to help the sheep when they are sick. And, of course, they learn how to clip a sheep's thick coat.

Rita and Tom like living on the
ranch. When their work is done, they
like to ride their horses, play games,
and read books. Once they even had a
ride in an airplane the firefighters
have for finding fires.

One day at the start of fall, Tom and
Rita put on riding boots and took their
horses out. They came back soon because
the sky got very black and full of dust.

Father was working on one of the
trucks. He had a rule: always keep the
trucks working well. Because Father was
so busy, he did not see the sky slowly
turning black. The dust was blowing,
and it was getting very cold.

The children called to Father to
look at the sky.

Father said, "I don't like the way the sky looks. Let's call on the radio and find out what is going on farther up the mountain."

Mother was already at the radio. She spoke to a neighbor who lived farther up the mountain. The neighbor said the dust was stopping, and it was starting to snow. He said a big snow was coming, and it would get very cold.

Father looked at Mother and said, "The sheep are on the mountain. We must get those sheep down."

The Big Snow

Tom and Rita were surprised to see such a big snow in the fall. But they knew when the snow was deep the sheep could not eat. They also knew that those sheep could get sick when it got cold so fast. The family would have to take the trucks up the mountain and bring the sheep back to the ranch.

The dust had stopped blowing, but the snow was falling fast. Tom and Rita put on their boots. Father called the ranch hands, Cal and Bob. They took lights and ropes from the shed and put them on the trucks. Tom and Rita fixed hot drinks for the trip.

Rita helped Cal sweep the snow off
the big truck. Bob helped Tom sweep the
snow from the small truck. As they all
took their places, Tom was thinking
about how he would play on his sled when
they were done.

It was farther than ten miles to
where the sheep were. The trucks moved
slowly. The wind made them sway from
side to side. Of course, they went even
more slowly up the steep hills. The
trip took a long time.

When they got up the mountain, Mother said, "It's a good thing those sheep like to keep together. That will help us find them in all this snow."

They did find the sheep all in one place. But even so, it took a long time before they could get them into the open trucks. At last they were done.

It was quite late when the trucks
got back to the ranch. Cal and Bob went
to open the shed where the sheep would
live that winter.

Mother and Father took off
their coats and boots. They went
to the kitchen to make hot drinks
and gingerbread.

Tom pulled off his coat and said,
"Hot gingerbread is going to be the best
thing about this day. Do you think it
will be done soon? I think it's too
late to take my sled out now."

Rita looked through the window at the
blanket of snow, and farther on, the
sheep shed. The snow was deep and
white. And because everybody was safe
and warm, it looked pretty.

As Rita took off her coat she said,
"Of course the gingerbread will be
good. But I know one thing that is even
better. The sheep are safe and warm,
and so are we."

Animals, Animals

Desert Animals

Some animals live in the desert. They live in homes made in the dirt. Desert animals need little water. They like living in dry places. Many desert animals hide during the day when the sun is very hot. They come out when the sun goes down because then it is quite cold.

Homes in the Desert

A **desert** is a dry, hot place. It's a place where it might not rain for a year. Many animals could not live in a hot, dry desert. But some do.

Desert rats can live in the desert, because they know where to hide from the sun's heat. They hide in homes they have dug under the ground in the dry dirt. They sleep in the day instead of coming out into the sun. Then they come out as the sun goes down and it is not so hot.

A **desert rabbit** can live in a home another animal has dug in the dirt, instead of building its own home. It's easy to move into a home that another animal has already dug.

When desert rabbits are not at home, they can hide from the sun under a cactus. They come out again when the sun is low and it is not too hot.

Some desert animals don't care about the heat. **Roadrunners** don't. Instead of hiding from the sun, roadrunners run during the dry, hot day. When a roadrunner stops running, it goes to its home under a low cactus.

Roadrunners run more than they fly. They run fast to catch mice and snakes for food. Roadrunners also run fast to get away from animals that like roadrunners for food.

Desert animals like the **mule deer** have no homes. Mule deer move all the time to find food. They don't need much water, but they do like to have some near them all the time.

Mule deer know that they must not go to the same water hole again and again, because there are some animals who like mule deer for food. But, if an animal does chase them, mule deer do not run. Instead, they get away fast by jumping on all four feet at the same time.

A **pack rat** makes a desert home that is low and might be as wide as three feet. First, a pack rat finds a dry place under a cactus to make a hole. Next, the rat moves sticks, dirt, and dry plants to make its new home. It will make trips again and again, bringing back more dirt and dry plants. Then, when the nest is ready, the pack rat places cactus plants at the door to keep animals out.

Last, the pack rat makes its home pretty. It likes shiny glass, old mirrors, and even rings and spoons. The pack rat puts those things all around its home.

Pack rats drop one thing at their feet to pick up another. At times, pack rats give things away instead of just taking things.

The pack rat will keep dry food as well as pretty things in its home. The pack rat's things will be safe from any animals in its home dug under a cactus.

The pack rat, like many desert animals, has a home that helps it live in this hot, dry place.

A Day in the Desert

Fred and Sam are roadrunners. They live next to a low cactus. Some desert animals hide from the sun, but not roadrunners. Fred and Sam like the heat. After running all day, Fred and Sam also like to drink lemonade.

Sam likes to look for snakes and mice for food. But Fred likes telling jokes much more than he likes looking for food in the dry dirt. Fred tells the same jokes again and again, instead of looking for food.

One day Fred said to Sam, "I don't like to spend all day looking for food when instead I could be telling jokes. I have a plan. Instead of looking again and again for mice and snakes, we can make a lemonade stand."

"Why do we need a lemonade stand?" asked Sam.

"Maybe we can get animals to bring us food and we will give them lemonade. Then I will have more time for jokes."

Sam said, "I'll help you get the stand ready, but I don't think animals will bring food to get lemonade."

As they were building the lemonade stand in the dry dirt, Fred said to Sam, "What do bugs keep water in?"

"Not that old joke again," said Sam.

"Bugs keep water in a bug jug. Get it? Get it?" laughed Fred.

Sam said, "Fred, instead of telling the same jokes again and again, help me move this sign. It's too low."

BUY LEMONADE
1 SNAKE OR 1 MOUSE
FOR ONE GLASS

At last the stand was ready, but, no animals came for the lemonade. Fred and Sam had jugs of lemonade, but no food.

Fred said, "We are not thinking! Many animals sleep all day. It's too hot for them to be out. They don't want lemonade now. We must find food instead of wishing animals will bring it to us."

So they went to find food. After they ate, they went home again.

Sam went to sleep as the sun set low in the sky. But Fred sat on his rug and made a new plan. He was thinking he might try a joke stand instead of a lemonade stand. He would keep it open when the desert animals were not sleeping.

And that is what he did!

The Animal Park

There are many wild animals at a large animal park. It's such a perfect place to see animals. The animals live almost as they do in the wild.

The Perfect Picture

When Paul makes a wish it's almost
always the same one. He wants to
take pictures of lions. The only lions
Paul sees are the ones in his large
picture books.

Paul does not like taking pictures of
tame animals, such as dogs and cats.
The perfect picture for Paul is a
picture of a lion.

Marie lives near Paul. One day she came over to play and said, "Why do you have such a sad look? It's such a perfect day."

Paul said, "It may be a perfect day for you. But I want to take pictures of lions. How can I be glad when there are no lions here?"

Marie laughed, "I know a perfect place to see animals. I'll call my Aunt Carol who works at the animal park. She may have time to help you."

The next day, Paul and Marie took a
bus. They got off the bus almost at the
gate of the large animal park. Aunt
Carol crossed the grass to say hello.

Aunt Carol said, "I am glad to see
you two. Paul, I hear you are looking
for lions. We have a fine lion family.
This park is the perfect place to see
almost any kind of wild animal."

"May we see the lions now?"
asked Paul.

Aunt Carol said, "You will see the lions soon. We have to cross the park in the jeep. I'll be glad to stop so that you may take pictures of animals you see on the way to the lions. Hear the snarls? The lions are out on the grass. Let's get in the jeep and go."

After a while, Paul asked Aunt Carol to stop the jeep. He saw three very large elephants. As he took a picture of the elephants, he could hear the lions. He was glad they were almost to the place where the lions lived.

As the jeep crossed the large park, Aunt Carol said, "The tall, dry grass here is almost like the grass in the wild. The large animals seem to like this dry grass."

Then as they came to the lions playing on the grass, Aunt Carol said, "I bet you will be glad to take pictures of the whole lion family. Just let the man count them first. We count them at food time to see that no lions are missing."

A man who worked at the zoo said, "I have counted and counted, and one lion is missing. The missing lion is such a little baby, it could get lost crossing the rocks and the grass."

Paul almost got to take his perfect picture. Now he could not.

The Missing Lion

Aunt Carol said, "The large lions trample the tall grass, but the little ones hide in it. If we let the mother out on the grass, she will find her missing baby."

Marie said, "Don't give up, Paul. I know you are going to snap a perfect picture as soon as the lion finds her baby."

The large mother lion crossed the grass where it was almost all trampled. She followed the trampled grass. When she could hear a little snarl she stopped. That snarl led her to her missing baby, sitting in the crack of a large rock.

The baby was glad to see its mother. It snarled almost like a little kitten. The glad mother licked the baby's fur. Then, like a perfect mother, she took her little one back over the grass.

Paul was glad to see the mother and baby lion again. He got so busy snapping pictures that he almost lost track of the time. He took a funny picture of the baby eating a snack.

"I think this little baby is happy to be back with its mother," laughed Paul.

When they were back home, Paul said to Marie, "I am glad these pictures will be ready in three days. I know they will be perfect."

When the pictures were ready,
Paul and Marie looked at them all.
When they saw the picture of the mother
lion bringing back her baby, they knew
they liked that one best.

Paul said, "This is such a good
picture. We will give it to your aunt.
This is the perfect picture!"

Just for You

See how fast you can say these funny lines. Saying them almost right does not count.

Sad Sam was such a sick snake when he snapped up seven soft snacks before sleeping.

Ron Roadrunner raced right around a round rock as he ran after a red rabbit.

To be read by the teacher

Homes

by Ilo Orleans

A dog lives in a kennel;
  A pig lives in a pen;
A horse lives in a stable;
  And a lion in a den.

A chicken lives inside a coop;
    And goldfish in a bowl;
And sheep are happy in a fold—
    A mole, inside a hole.

The turtle lives inside his shell;
    The thrush lives in a nest;
And I live in a little house;
    For ME that is the best!

Who's in Rabbit's House?

by Verna Aardema

Long ago, Rabbit lived in a house near a lake. She liked to sit at her door and see the animals come to drink. But one day when she came back to her house she could not get in.

Something in the house said, "I am the Long One. I break mountains and trample on elephants. Go away, or I will trample on you!"

Rabbit said, "That's my house! Come out of it at once!"

But the Long One would not come out!

Rabbit sat down to think.

Frog hopped up and said with a soft cheep, "I can get that wild animal out."

Rabbit said, "No! You are so small! Do you think that you can do what I can not? I don't like you. Go away!"

Frog hopped off. But she did not go far. She wondered what Rabbit would do.

Then Jackal came. He wanted to help.

"Who's in Rabbit's house?" he asked.

Something in the house said, "I am the Long One. I break mountains and trample on elephants. Go away, or I will trample on you!"

Jackal put sticks around the house. He was going to light a fire.

But Rabbit said, "No fire! Go away!"

So Jackal went <u>pa</u>, <u>pa</u>, <u>pa</u>, down to the lake to drink.

Leopard came by. He wanted to help.

"Who's in Rabbit's house?" he asked.

Something in the house said, "I am the Long One. I break mountains and trample on elephants. Go away, or I will trample on you!"

Leopard jumped on the house. He made little holes in the top, so it looked just like a net. Snip, snip, snip!

"Stop! Go away!" cried Rabbit.

So Leopard went creep, creep, creep, down to the lake to drink.

An elephant came. He wanted to help.

"Who's in Rabbit's house?" he asked.

Something in the house said, "I am the Long One. I break mountains and trample on elephants. Go away, or I will trample on you!"

Elephant said, "You will not trample on me! I'll throw you into the lake, house and all!"

He put his head down low and went <u>ras</u>, <u>ras</u>, <u>ras</u>. He was going to swing right through the little house when Rabbit jumped on his nose.

Elephant shook his head. So away
went Rabbit. . . . <u>WEO!</u> spinning
up and up. Splash!

Elephant said, "That's the end of the
Long One!"

"But you knocked <u>Rabbit</u> into the
lake!" Frog said.

Rabbit came back, all wet. She still
was not in her house, and she was sad.

Frog said, "I know how to help you."

"Then please try," said Rabbit.

Frog snarled, "I am Cobra! Come out of that house. Or I will creep under the door and get you!"

The door opened. And out came Caterpillar!

Caterpillar said, "I am only Caterpillar. Don't let Cobra get me! I was only playing a joke!"

Rabbit said, "Caterpillar, Cobra was only Frog."

Then Frog laughed so hard, all one could see of her was her big laugh.

And Rabbit sat at her door once more.

Books To Read

Down the Road by Joan Lesikin

Where can a snake and a
turtle live together?
You will be surprised!

From DOWN THE ROAD by Joan Lesikin. Copyright © 1978
by Joan Lesikin. Published by Prentice-Hall, Inc., Englewood
Cliffs, NJ 07632. Reprinted by permission.

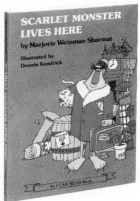

Scarlet Monster Lives Here
by Marjorie Sharmat

What will Scarlet Monster's
new neighbors think of her?

Cover from SCARLET MONSTER LIVES HERE by Marjorie
Weinman Sharmat. Illustrated by Dennis Kendrick. Text
copyright © 1979 by Marjorie Weinman Sharmat. Illustrations
copyright © 1979 by Dennis Kendrick. Reprinted by
permission of Harper & Row, Publishers, Inc.

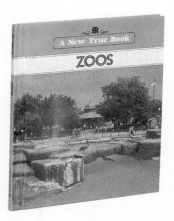

Zoos by Karen Jacobsen

This is a true book about
zoo animals. The pictures
are wonderful.

Cover from ZOOS by Karen Jacobson reprinted by permission
of David J. Maenza.

Water Wonders

The Wild Wet Land

A swamp is a wet land. There are trees, plants, and animals everywhere in the swamp. A swamp is a good place for some animals to live. Alligators and some snakes live in swamps.

Swamp Animals in Danger

Alan's house is near a swamp. Many animals live in the swamp. Alan likes to learn about how the animals live and what happens to them. He likes going to work with his neighbor Penny. Her job is to keep track of the animals that live in the swamp. Penny knows when animals are hurt or in danger.

One day Penny read that people had been fixing swamp land so they could build homes there. People were taking out water and putting in dry dirt to build on. Penny was afraid the animals would not have enough room to live if people took the swamp land.

Penny said to Alan, "I don't want snakes or alligators to be hurt or in danger. That is what will happen if people build homes in swamps."

"What can we do to help save the animals?" asked Alan.

Alan helped Penny write to people who might help them. Some of these people worked on radio and TV. Penny and Alan said they wanted to keep their swamp safe from people building there. They did not want swamp animals to be hurt or in danger. Penny and Alan asked the people to help them by coming on a motor boat trip to see the swamp.

Four people called Penny to say they would come to see the swamp.

Alan and Penny took the motor boat out to plan the trip. Penny had a map of the swamp. She showed Alan how to mark each place they would show the people. Alan was a little afraid when they found where the alligators lived. But he marked the place on the map. Then Penny showed him an alligator.

They saw the alligator chew on some plants it found in the water. It put the plants it had been chewing on land. Then it went sliding into the water to pull up more plants to chew. After that, it put each plant up on land and went back for more. This happened over and over again.

Penny said, "You look a little afraid, Alan. You don't have to be afraid. This alligator is too busy to hurt you. You are not in any danger."

As Alan and Penny went back home, Alan was wondering why the alligator had been pulling up all those plants.

Alligators Everywhere

When they were ready to begin the trip around the swamp, Penny said, "Alan, blow the horn! The horn will tell people to get into the motor boat."

Alan beeped the horn and people came to the boat. They all found places to sit. Penny talked about what they would see. Alan looked at the marks on the map and wondered what the alligators would be doing.

Soon Alan found the worn grass that
was near the alligator's home. Alan had
been a little afraid of what he would
find. Now he could see why Penny had
not been afraid of the alligator and all
the torn plants. The alligator was a
mother alligator. She had been building
a home for the baby alligators.

There were alligators everywhere.
Seven baby alligators followed the
mother down to the water. Penny
found more baby alligators in the water.

Alan said, "Baby alligators are not afraid of the water! They follow their mother everywhere!"

After they had looked at all the baby alligators, Penny said, "Now we will take a trip around the swamp. You will see snakes, turtles, wonderful trees, and plants. You will see tall water grass and many thorn plants. In the swamp some trees have a dark green bark. Some trees here are not like trees you see on dry land."

When they got back to land, the
people who had been on the trip found
ways to tell about what happened in the
swamp. One woman went on the radio.
One man talked about it on TV. People
started to work to keep the swamp
a safe place for the animals to live.

Penny and Alan did not know if
swamps everywhere were as wonderful
as their swamp. But they were glad
they were helping to keep one place
safe for baby alligators to grow up.

An Aquarium

Anywhere you go in an Aquarium
you can be certain to see many kinds
of fish. You might even see a penguin
or a flying fish.

Fish Wishes

Each day, coming from school, Anna walked by a pet shop. Each day she stopped to watch some little fish. They lived in a large aquarium among many plants and rocks.

Anna was certain she wanted a fish, but she had not saved enough to buy one. Then one day Anna read a sign.

The City Aquarium was going to give away fish from ponds near the city. Children anywhere in the city could get one. They just had to make a safe home for their fish.

The next day Anna went to the Aquarium. The building was a zoo for fish. There were many children there. Anna met Don, a boy from school.

Mrs. Gates worked at the Aquarium. She showed them around. Mrs. Gates said, "I am certain you will see fish here that you could only see at an Aquarium. Sometimes these fish come from places far away. After you look around, I'll tell you how to build an aquarium for your fish. Your fish will come from a pond or lake near here."

Don watched a fish that had a funny mouth and no eyes. This fish lived in caves under the water without any light.

While Anna and Don were watching the fish, Anna made her mouth look like the fish's mouth. Anna looked just like the fish without eyes. Don laughed until his sides hurt.

Then Mrs. Gates said to all the children, "The fish that live in deep water live without bright light.

"Sometimes bright light can burn a fish's eyes. In the City Aquarium a soft light keeps those fish from hurting their eyes."

Mrs. Gates said, "Now that you have watched many fish, let's talk about how to keep your pet fish happy. First, to make an aquarium you must wash the glass until it's very clean. Dirt can burn a fish's eyes or mouth. Then, let the water stand until it's as warm as the room. Next, your fish needs a soft light that will not hurt its eyes.

"It's fun to feed your fish! But watch out! Too much food can sometimes be a danger to your pet.

"As soon as you are certain your aquarium is just right, come and pick out a fish."

Anna's Aquarium

As Anna and Don walked home, Don said, "I had fun at the Aquarium. But I don't want a pet fish. I think I would like a snake from the pet shop instead."

Anna was a little afraid of snakes. She was certain that a pond fish would be perfect for her.

Anna left Don and went to start her aquarium. Anna would have to look in the garage for what she needed. It was almost dark when she got home. Even without much light to work by Anna went to look for a jar and some shells.

Anna looked everywhere in the garage until she found a large glass jar. Then, among some old boxes she found a box of shells. She took the shells and the jar to the house.

She cleaned the jar and the shells until they shined. She did not want dirt to burn her fish's eyes or mouth.

Then Anna went to the pet shop and got green plants for the fish to nibble.

When Anna was ready to go to the Aquarium, she put on her skirt with the shark on it to show Mrs. Gates. Then she went to the Aquarium to get her fish. When Mrs. Gates saw Anna's skirt she asked if Anna would like a shark for a pet.

Anna laughed and said, "No, I don't have room anywhere for a shark. I'll just take this little pond fish home."

Anna put the new fish in her room. She watched it swim among the shells and plants and wondered if the fish was also watching her.

She was certain it was.

Tricia's Fish

by Lee Bennett Hopkins

Whenever I go fishing
I keep on wishing
I wouldn't catch so many!

Because—
Ralph and Ron and Ricky,
Martha, Marge and Mickie

don't
ever, ever
catch any!

Some people think watching fish in an aquarium is fun. Sometimes people go fishing for the fun of catching a fish.

What if you happened to be a fish instead of a boy or girl? What would you do for fun?

Would you go to a people zoo? Or, would you watch fish on TV?

Make a picture of a fish family having fish fun. Then color your picture.

Fish Fun

Have you ever been to a fishing contest? People in the contests get prizes for catching the biggest fish. It's fun to see people by the river, wishing for fish.

The Contest at the River

Holly and Mike were sitting at the table. Dad was reading the paper.

Mike turned to Holly and said with his hands, "You draw so much!"

Holly stopped drawing. She needed to use both hands to talk to Mike. Mike could not hear, so the family used hand signs when they spoke.

Holly said, "I don't draw all the time. Sometimes I go fishing. But Mom said I draw great pictures. So this fish will be for her."

Dad signed to both Mike and Holly, "I see the city is having a fishing contest for boys and girls. They will have a group for big boys and girls and one for little boys and girls. They will give prizes for catching the biggest fish. They will pick a winner from each group."

Mike asked, "Have you ever been to a fishing contest, Dad?"

Dad said, "No. But I'll bet you and Holly would be great at fishing. Holly can use my pole. Mom has one too. Hers is new. You can use hers."

Holly said, "Let's go get the poles and hooks, Mike. We can not go to the contest without them."

As they went into the garage Holly said, "How will we ever find poles in this mess?"

Mike said, "Here is Mom's pole. And here is Dad's too."

Holly said, "Here are some hooks. You must watch out with hooks. It hurts if you ever stick one in your hand. Now let's find some bait."

Mike asked, "What will we use for bait?"

Holly said, "We must go to the field and look for a big stone."

Mike said, "How do we use a stone? Do we hit the fish on its head?"

Holly said, "Sometimes you are funny. You look under the stone until you find a worm. I am certain the best worms are under the biggest stones."

Holly was right, and they each dug up great big worms until the jar was full.

The Great Fish Dream

The next morning Mike said, "I had
a great dream. We went to the river
and I got the biggest fish ever to bite. I
did it without using any worms for bait."

Holly said, "With all these worms,
we will have enough bait. Let's go!"

First they walked to the pizza shop
to get their lunch. Then they walked on
until they came to the river. There were
groups of people everywhere.

Holly said, "There is a small group of people by those flat stones. Let's fish there. We may get a bite, if your bright shirt does not scare the fish."

Mike sat on his stone and Holly sat on hers. They put worms on the hooks.

Mike said, "My shirt will not scare the fish. They might even like my red shirt better than a worm."

Holly looked at Mike and said, "That is not true. I am certain fish like worms best."

Then they sat by the river, watching and wishing. Sometimes they lost their bait and had to put on new bait. They watched the lines, but there was not a bite or a nibble.

A boy in a group next to them got
a fish.

Holly said, "That boy's fish is
big, but we might still catch the
biggest fish."

When they had been fishing almost
all day and still had no fish, Holly said,
"I just used the last worm. How can
we fish without bait?"

Mike said, "I have a great plan. Use the pizza from lunch."

"But that is my pizza. You ate yours already," said Holly.

"Just put it on your hook. I am certain something will happen," said Mike with a grin.

So Holly put the pizza on her hook and put her line back into the river. Soon something did happen. She got a big fish to bite.

"You will win a prize!" said Mike.

"Maybe we will win a prize. Your plan got the fish," said Holly.

Mike did not care if they got a prize. He had a great time.

As Holly looked at the biggest fish she had ever had on her line, she said to Mike, "Your dream came true! We did get a fish without using worms for bait. What a great fish it is!"

"Think Fast"

Help, Help

Sometimes people need to think fast!
If you were to smell smoke or if people
were hurt, would you know how to help?
Even if you felt afraid you might either
call for help or get help. But to be
safe, you need to think fast.

The New Neighborhood Hall

The day the new neighborhood hall opened, the city was to give out prizes. The first ten children to get to the hall that morning would get T-shirts. The next ten children would get buttons. Ruth and Kathy wanted to get either one.

Kathy said, "The hall will not open until ten. Let's get to the hall by eight. That way we can get either a T-shirt or a button."

"I'll see you at eight," said Ruth.

The next morning they got to the door of the hall at eight. Kathy said, "It smells awful here. Do you smell smoke?"

Ruth said, "Yes! Black smoke is coming from the hall. I can hear the smoke alarm. If it's a fire, we should get help fast."

Kathy said, "You go that way and I'll go this way. One of us will find help."

The girls were scared. They did not want the new neighborhood hall to burn.

Neighborhood Hall

OPENING!
VOLUNTEER
HELP
WANTED

Kathy saw a police car parked on the street and called, "Help! Police! See that smoke? An awful thing is happening. The new hall is on fire."

The policewoman in the car said, "I'll call in the alarm on the police radio. That is the fastest thing to do. It won't take long for the firefighters to come."

Kathy was glad that the alarm got called in so fast.

The policewoman said, "We should hear the sirens soon. I'll stop the traffic. Thanks for your help."

Ruth ran down the street and found a fire-alarm call box. But, she was too small to push the button. Ruth saw Mrs. Jones coming.

Ruth said, "Mrs. Jones, there is the most awful fire. We should push the alarm button, but I am too small."

Mrs. Jones pushed the alarm button.

Ruth wondered how much longer it would be before they would hear sirens and see fire trucks. Would the hall burn down?

The Fire

Kathy and Ruth met back near the hall. Soon they could hear sirens. Three fire trucks came, one large truck and two smaller ones. The Fire Chief was in the smallest truck. That truck was fastest. It seemed to fly by the stopped traffic with its siren going.

The smallest fire truck was nearest
the hall. The firefighters from that
truck hooked up a hose to spray water.
There was smoke everywhere. Most of the
people watching were certain the hall
would burn to the ground.

But it was not much longer before
there was only a little smoke and
no fire. The big truck left. The
traffic started to move again.

The Chief asked, "Who pushed the alarm button? This fire would have been awful if it had burned longer."

The policewoman said, "Chief, Ruth and Kathy each called in an alarm."

The Chief said, "It's sad that the neighborhood hall won't open today. However, thanks to Ruth and Kathy's fast thinking, it will open soon."

The next day the Chief went to Ruth and Kathy's school. All the children met in the big school hall.

The Chief said, "We would all have felt awful if the new hall had burned to the ground. Ruth and Kathy's fast thinking saved the hall. If you are ever in a building and you smell smoke, you should think fast and get out, even if you don't see the fire. Then you should call for help or go to a fire-alarm call box. But always think before you run."

The Chief said, "As a reward for their fast thinking, I am giving Ruth and Kathy firefighter hats."

Ruth and Kathy were surprised. Firefighter's hats were even better than T-shirts or buttons.

To be read by the teacher

Fireman

by Frank Asch

In his black hat
He drives a red truck
Through a red light
On his way to fight
The red and yellow flames.

Firefighters have hats that help them in their work. Their hats are made to let water run off them. Their hats are hard to keep things from hurting their heads.

What kind of hat would help you in school? How about a thinking hat?

Draw a picture of a funny school hat. Tell how it will help you do something.

◆ Getting Started

Good Thinking!

People don't always do what they should. Sometimes we think people should do one thing, but they do another. At these times good thinking may help people we love.

Hank's Good Thinking

Hank had a job after school. He took
care of his little brother Joe. Most
days Hank met Joe as soon as school was
out. They walked home together.

One day Hank's mother asked Hank to
do something for her right after school.
Mother asked Joe to sit at his school
door until Hank came. Joe would have to
sit only a little while. However, when
Hank got to where Joe should have been,
Joe was not there. Hank felt angry.

Hank knew that Joe was a dreamer. Joe meant to be good, but if there was something he loved to do he did it. One thing Joe loved was making buildings with his blocks.

Hank was certain Joe must be at home making a tall building. Hank ran home, but Joe was not there. Hank was angry.

Mrs. Blake was the neighbor above them. She was a painter. She liked to paint pictures of buildings. Hank went to see if Joe was there.

Mrs. Blake said, "No, Joe is not here. He must be doing something else."

Then Hank went to call his mother. He always called her at work when he got home. This time Hank said he could not find Joe. It bothered him.

Mother said, "I am sure you can think where Joe might be. You must try hard!"

Hank felt angry and unhappy, but he sat down to think. Then he knew!

Hank ran until he came to the place where the tallest building in the city was going up. There was Joe. He was watching the builders working far above the ground.

Hank took Joe home. For most of the trip home Joe talked about how fantastic it would be to be a builder working far above the ground. Joe said he meant to sit at school until Hank came, but he wanted to see the building.

When they got home Mother and Dad were home from work and hugged both of them. However, they were angry at Joe. Joe had to go to bed right after they ate. Hank got to stay up late. Mother and Dad were proud of his good thinking.

The Fantastic Mix-Up

Mrs. Mole could not see very well.
Even though Mrs. Mole's eyes bothered
her, she pushed her wagon to the food
shop each morning to find the best foods
for her family. She was unhappy if the
food was not perfect. Since she could
not see well enough to shop, she had to
touch each of the vegetables to be sure
the ones she picked were perfect.

Mrs. Mole, whose shopping wagon looked like most shopping wagons, did not bother to take it into the shop. Most shoppers, like Mrs. Pig and Mr. Cat, left their wagons at the door too.

One day Mrs. Mole parked her wagon and went to shop for apples for her fantastic apple cake. She touched all the apples to be sure to get perfect ones. Then the shop helper put them into her wagon.

Soon after Mrs. Mole started on her trip home, Mrs. Pig came out of the shop. She looked at her wagon and called, "Help! Police!"

The Police Chief said, "What is it?"

Mrs. Pig said, "Help me! I have a sack of apples instead of my pet duck!"

The Chief, who was a fast thinker, said, "I'll talk to the shop helper."

The Chief came out and said, "I know where your duck is. I'll tell you about it on the way. Come with me."

Mrs. Mole was a fast walker, and by this time she was home. She put her hand into her wagon to take out her apples. But she felt something else. The something else she touched was softer than apples. It was a baby duck.

"Whose duck is this? Whose duck could this be?" asked Mrs. Mole.

As Mrs. Pig got to Mrs. Mole's house, Mrs. Mole was hugging the little duck.

Mrs. Mole said, "Don't be angry about this awful mix-up! Please sit down, and we will have some lemonade."

Mrs. Pig said, "Now that I have my pet duck back I am not unhappy. You are the kindest mole!"

The Chief knew that Mrs. Mole had not meant to take the little duck. So he was glad that everybody was happy now.

Safe from the Sea

Holland is a country that is right next to the sea. The country has big walls that protect it from the sea water. The walls are called dikes. Without the dikes to protect Holland, much of the country would soon be under water.

Hans Saves the Country

Hans Wants to Whistle

STORYTELLER: The play begins in Holland a long time ago, at Hans's house. Hans's mother and sister are ready to rake so they can plant seeds.

MOM: Hans! What are you doing? Come help.

HANS: I was just looking at the sea.

KATY: No he is not! He is trying to whistle with his finger in his mouth like a boy at school.

HANS: Not one finger! Two fingers! I would love to whistle like that. Every time I try I am sure I will get it, but then I don't.

MOM: If you want your fingers to be helpful, you can help with the raking.

DAD (Comes out of the house): Look at the sea today. It is so wild. If it were not for the dikes holding back the sea, then every house and road would wash away.

KATY: Dad, did you help build every one of the dikes?

DAD: No, I certainly did not build every dike. Most of them are even older than I am.

HANS: One day I would love to help build dikes to protect us. But I would be happy for now if I could whistle with my fingers.

DAD: Hans, for now put your fingers to work on the rake. You can work on your whistle another time. After we are done planting, your mother wants you to do something else.

MOM: Hans! Aunt Lou and Greta want your sister Katy to come to their house. Greta loves to play with Katy.

DAD: Yes, Hans. Please walk Katy there. Your aunt would love to see you too. But then you should dash right home.

HANS: I won't have any time to play. I will be mostly dashing there and dashing home.

DAD: Take the dike road. It is faster by the sea. We want you home before dark. Don't walk too slowly.

HANS: Come along, Katy. Greta will surely be unhappy if you are late.

STORYTELLER: So Hans and Katy set out for a long walk on the dike road.

The Trip to Aunt Lou's

STORYTELLER: On the road Hans and Katy see Jan, a boy they both know.

JAN: Hello! Hans, how is your finger whistle coming along?

HANS: Every time I try, Katy laughs and I get angry.

JAN: I am sure you will get it soon. Keep trying. So long!

KATY: Are you angry because I laugh at your whistle? I won't do it again.

KATY: I felt some sea spray touch me. Can the sea come above the dike?

HANS: No, Katy. Every one of these dikes protects the country from the sea. The water won't touch you.

KATY: We are here now! I see Aunt Lou and Greta. Hans, try to whistle with your fingers for them.

HANS: I would love to. But you know every time I try, my fingers just won't work.

AUNT: How is my little Katy?

KATY: I am fine.

GRETA: I am so glad you are here.
We can play most of the day.

AUNT: Hans, you are growing bigger and
bigger every time I see you.

HANS: Yes, I am growing, but I can
hardly even whistle with my
fingers yet.

AUNT: Surely you will whistle soon if
you just try harder.

HANS: I should go now or else I
won't be home before dark.

AUNT: Thanks for bringing Katy over.

STORYTELLER: Hans set out on the dike
road. Just before dark he met a
man and a woman who spoke to him.

MAN: It's late, boy. Dash home.

WOMAN: It's almost dark. Run home.

HANS: Yes, yes. I will run home.
What is that? Water? There is a
hole in the dike. Help! The man
and woman have left. I must
stop the hole. I will put a rock in
it. No, it won't hold. What else
can I use? My fingers. I'll put my
fingers in until help comes. Help!

STORYTELLER: Hans was cold and wet but he did not take his fingers out of the dike. In the morning he saw the same man and woman on the road again. This time he put his fingers in his mouth and gave a big whistle.

MAN: Where is that whistle coming from?

WOMAN: It's that boy. Who are you?

HANS: I am Hans. There is a hole in the dike. Get my dad. He will surely know how to fix it.

STORYTELLER: The man and woman went to get Hans's father. They found Hans's whole family out looking for Hans. They all came to the road.

DAD: Hans, I am thankful you are safe.

HANS: I certainly meant to be on time.
But I found a hole in the dike and
I put my fingers in to stop the sea.

MOM: How bravely he helped us.

AUNT: The whole country might have
washed away if you had not helped.

JAN: We are all safe, thanks to Hans.
A whistle can be very useful.

KATY: Hans, I am glad you **could** whistle
when you had to.

New and Fantastic

Make it New

Think about the things you do each day. Can you think of a new way to do them? Do you suppose you could come up with a whole new way to do something?

The Magic Cutter

The winter had been long for Rabbit, Squirrel, and Fox. Now it was a warm day, and there was little snow left on the ground. The animals were thinking how wonderful it would be to go to the lake for food.

Rabbit looked out from the doorway of the house and said, "It's almost springtime. Indeed it is. The road to the lake must be open now. Suppose we go to the lake for food."

As they got to the road, Squirrel said, "Look at those rocks blocking our road."

Rabbit said, "This is the only road between our house and the lake. We must move those rocks. Except, I don't know how we can."

Fox said, "Move these rocks? Even though I have done pushups all winter, these rocks are too big for me to move. We can go to Owl's house without using the road. Maybe Owl will help us think of what to do."

So the animals walked through the
deep mud to where Owl lived. Owl lived
in an old schoolhouse on a hill. When
Owl learned why they had come she said
she would help.

Owl said, "I suppose what you need is
a machine. Yes, indeed, you need a
magic cutter. A magic cutter will make
all the big rocks small enough to move.
Don't lose any time. Make a list of
what you need."

Squirrel took out her notebook and
said, "What should we put on our list?"

Owl said, "First, put a curtain on your list. Next, you need two snowshoes. And last, put wood on your list. Now bring those things to me, and I'll help you build the magic cutter."

Rabbit, Squirrel, and Fox started home through the mud. They were each wondering if Owl had made a mistake about the things on the list. They could not imagine that these things could make a magic cutter machine.

As they walked, Rabbit said, "Let's not lose any more time wondering what Owl will do. Suppose we just find the curtains, the snowshoes, and the wood."

Yes, indeed, that is just what they would do!

The New Machine

Fox said, "Come to the shed with me before it gets too dark. My old snowshoes are out there on a rack. I know where they are, but I cannot get them down without help."

They all went through the mud to the shed. Fox and Squirrel were holding the ladder so Rabbit could pull the snowshoes off the rack.

They went back to the house. Then Rabbit and Squirrel took the curtains from their windows. Now they had all the things on the list except the wood.

Squirrel gave them the wood from her bed. Now they had all the things on the list and Owl would help them.

In the morning they went to Owl's house. She was on the playground making the last snowball of winter. She started to tell them that the magic cutter machine would cut and crush rocks, but Fox stopped her.

Fox said, "Owl, you have a good plan, except you made one mistake. Wood will not crush or cut rock. Suppose we fix your machine to throw rocks instead of crushing them. Let's not lose any more time. I want to try the new plan."

They all said Fox's plan was the one
to try. So when they got to the road
they all helped set up the machine. All
except Owl, of course, who was still
trying to tell everybody what to do.

They pushed the machine under one big
rock. Then Squirrel gave the countdown:
Three, Two, One, Jump! Fox and Rabbit
together jumped onto one snowshoe. The
rock went flying.

They had made no mistakes. The machine was perfect. They pushed the machine under more rocks. Fox and Rabbit jumped again and again until the road was open. Then Rabbit and Fox, carrying the machine between them, led the animals down to the lake. They all ate and ate.

After they ate, the animals took the machine home. They put the wood back in Squirrel's bed. They put the curtains back on the window. They even put the snowshoes back on the old rack in the shed. They sat by the fire and were happy with their day's work.

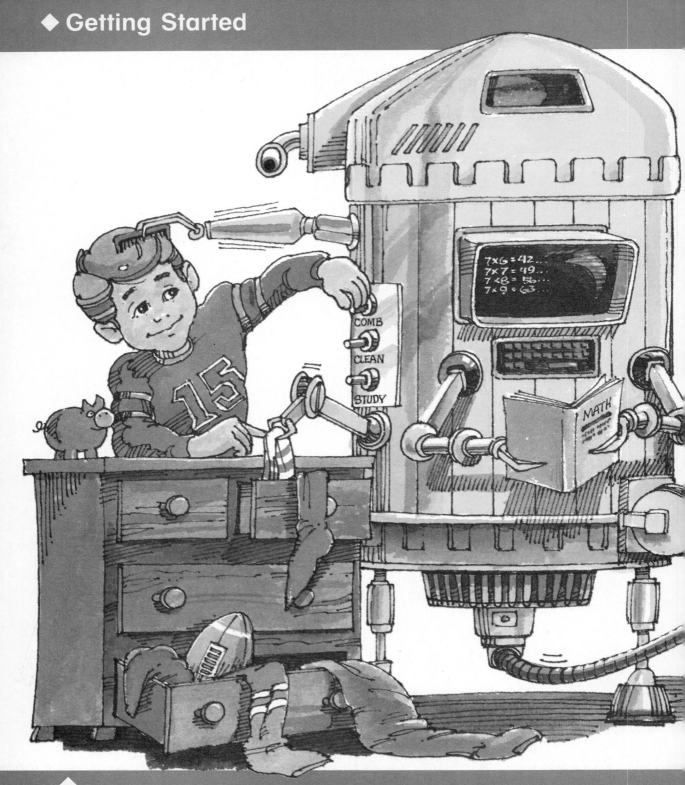

New and Better

Are you happy when you learn something new? It's fun to add new things to what you already know. People working together can sometimes learn how to make a good thing even better. At least they can try!

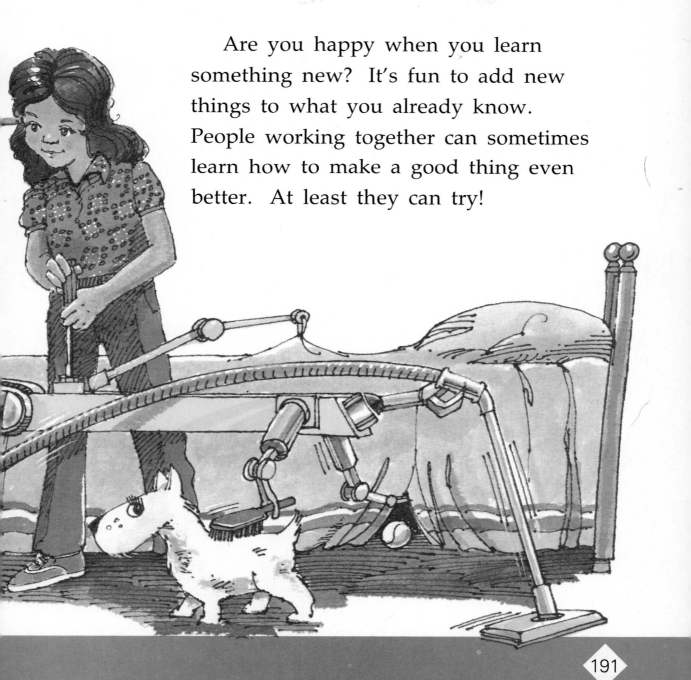

Let's Talk

Nina got comfortable at the desk in the hall. She had so many secrets to tell her neighbor, Patsy, that she called Patsy and asked her to come over.

But Patsy said she had to babysit. Patsy's mother said that since Nina had a cold she could not come there.

So the girls talked for a long time. At last, Nina's sister Rosa and her brother Rick grew angry. Nina was still not ready to hang up.

After a while, Rick said, "Nina, you and Patsy shouldn't talk so much. Hang up and let me make at least one call."

Rosa added, "Nina, you keep the line busy all day."

"You two shouldn't tell me what to do," Nina said.

Then their dad came in saying, "That's enough! I don't like this angry talk between brothers and sisters. You may get calls. But you cannot make any more calls, at least not until you three get along better."

Nina said, "I have to hang up now, Patsy. My dad won't let me make any more calls. We need another way to talk so we can tell our secrets. Do you suppose you can get a ball, some paper, a pen, and a hat?"

Patsy said she could.

Nina said, "Good! Then take all those things to your bedroom window."

Patsy could not imagine what Nina was planning. But at least the plan seemed as if it would be fun.

Nina said, "When you get to your window, open it. Then write a note and tie it to a ball. Throw the ball in my direction. I'll catch the ball in a hat. Then I'll read your note and write another one to throw back to you. You catch the ball in your hat."

The first part of the plan worked. Patsy got the ball in the right direction. The ball landed in the hat. Nina did the same thing, except Patsy did not catch the ball in the hat.

Patsy called Nina.

Nina said, "I know where we made our mistake. At least part of our plan worked. Suppose we make a better plan." Nina got comfortable to think.

Patsy said, "Let's try flying machines. Hang up and I'll fly an airplane with a note in your direction. It shouldn't take long to make one."

Soon Patsy's airplane was flying in Nina's direction. It was great, except it landed right on the ground.

Patsy called Nina again. Patsy said, "The airplane was perfect. The only mistake was throwing it on the ground. Let's add to the good part of our plan."

Nina said, "Hang up. I know what to add to the plan. I'll see you soon."

Nina went to Rick and Rosa and said, "If you help me, Patsy and I will not tie up the line again. Do either of you have some rope?"

Rick said, "Yes. This is all yours."

Rosa added some of hers too. The three of them worked together to tie knots in the rope. It grew longer and longer. Soon it grew long enough to go between the two houses.

Dad looked in and said, "I love to see our family working together. You may all make calls again."

"Dad, if this machine of ours works, I won't make any more calls," said Nina.

The rope was long enough now to make a ring between the two houses. Nina and Patsy pinned little notes to the rope and pulled it in a circle between them.

After a long time they said, "Time to hang up! Let's talk in the morning."

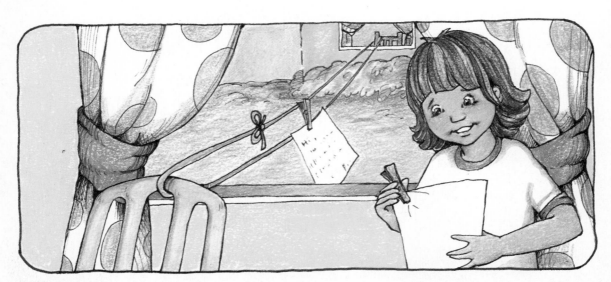

A Star for Ned

Ned was happy. He wanted to see his teacher, Mrs. Moon. In Mrs. Moon's class, children got stars with their names on them when they learned something new. Ned would get a star because he had learned how to tie a new knot. Now he could tie knots to make plant hangers for the plants that grew in their room.

Ned met Adam and they walked to class. Their room was at the end of the hall. When they got there, they saw a new teacher at Mrs. Moon's desk. They were sure they had made a mistake and this room was not theirs.

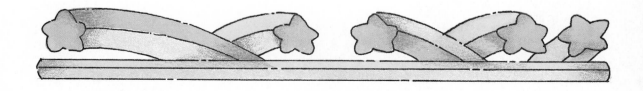

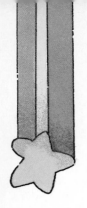

The new teacher said, "Come in.
Please hang up your coats."

Ned said, "Is this our room? He is
not our teacher. What's going on here?"

The new teacher said, "I am Mr. Day.
Mrs. Moon is sick. She will be out for
at least three days."

Ned was sad. He liked Mrs. Moon.
He did not know Mr. Day. Also,
Mr. Day did not know that Ned should
get a star for learning to tie new knots.

Mr. Day said, "Let's begin our morning. I'll call each of your names to learn who you are."

Then Mr. Day said, "Here are your directions. One part of the class will add this set of numbers and one part of the class will add that set of numbers."

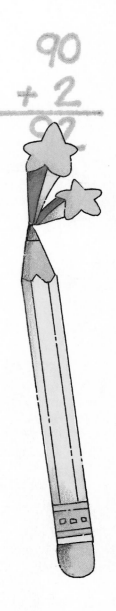

Adam and Ned got comfortable at their desks. The adding was very hard. Mr. Day looked at theirs.

"That's very good," said Mr. Day. He took their work to hang on the wall.

Adam said, "You don't have your star yet, but at least the new teacher knows you can add."

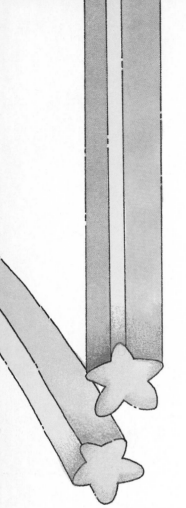

Mr. Day said, "Here are your next directions. Part of the class will go to music now and part will read with me. Then we'll all go to the park."

Adam and Ned took their books and their workbooks from their desks. They enjoyed the part of the book they read together. They did some work in their workbooks together too.

After reading was over, Adam asked, "Ned, why don't you show Mr. Day your knots? He might give you a star."

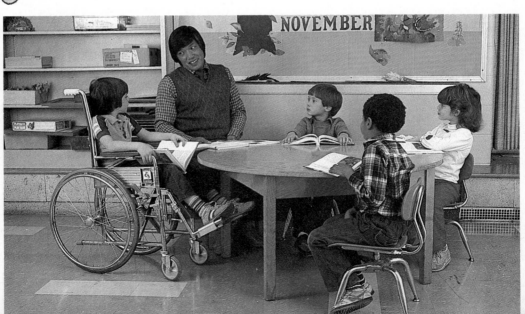

Before Ned could talk to Mr. Day, he said, "Time to go to the park. Take your coats."

When they got to the park, there was another class at the park too. Ned and Adam played ball. When it was time to go, many coats were on the ground.

"Are these ours?" asked Mr. Day.

Ned said, "Some of these coats are ours. But some are theirs. I can help give them out."

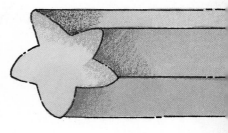

On the way back to school Mr. Day thanked Ned for helping with the coats. Ned asked if Mr. Day ever gave stars for learning new things, even if they were not things learned in class.

Mr. Day asked what Ned had learned. Then he watched Ned tie his new knots and said, "That's great!"

When they got back to class, Mr. Day made Ned a big yellow sun.

Ned asked, "Why don't you give stars like Mrs. Moon does?"

Mr. Day laughed and said, "I did give you a star. Did you know that the sun is a star? It's the only star we see during the day."

Ned was very happy with his sun. He and Adam laughed about getting suns from Mr. Day and stars from Mrs. Moon.

As Ned walked home he was thinking how much fun it was to learn new things. Learning to tie the new knots was even better than getting suns or stars.

Walking

by Lilian Moore

I stop—
       it stops, too.
It goes when I do.

Over my shoulder I can see
The moon is taking a walk with me.

Think of a job you don't like to do. How would you like a machine to do the job for you? Draw a picture of the machine. Write about what it does.

The Mouse and the Stonecutter

by Nancy De Roin

Long ago a stonecutter worked in a secret mountain cave that had walls of wonderful stone. Each day he worked crushing and cracking the wall into small stones that he took home.

By the time he got home, the stars were out. His little house was dark and cold. After he ate a little bread and milk, he shined stones until they looked as clear as a mirror. He could buy all the food he needed with those stones.

One day while the stonecutter was out of his house, a mouse came in and nibbled on some bread. It ran behind a curtain when the stonecutter came back.

The stonecutter saw holes in the bread and said, "A mouse nibbled this. Well, there's enough bread for us both."

The next day, after the stonecutter left, the mouse ate some more bread. While the mouse ate, it looked around and saw that the house was very messy.

The mouse said, "The stonecutter lets me eat his bread. I can be helpful to him. I'll clean his house."

The mouse got very busy cleaning. When the stonecutter came back, the mouse was standing bravely by the door.

The stonecutter said, "Little mouse, you have made the house as shiny as my best stones. You have worked hard, now come and eat."

And so it came to be that the mouse cleaned for the stonecutter, and each day the stonecutter fed the mouse.

One day, while the stonecutter was out, a cat came in and got the mouse.

The cat snarled and said, "You are mine. I will have you for lunch."

The mouse cried, "Let me go, and I can bring you food today and every day."

"All right! But I want some meat and milk fast," said the cat.

So the mouse fed the cat part of its own food that day and every day. The cat made the mouse bring more and more food. The little mouse grew very thin. And the stonecutter wondered why.

One day, the stonecutter did not go to work. Instead, he watched from behind a curtain as the cat took food.

When the cat left, the stonecutter said to the mouse, "Mouse, that's the last food you will give away! That cat thinks it was born to be fed by mice. But I have a trick that will take care of that."

The stonecutter shined a block of stone until it was clear as glass. He cut a hole in it just big enough for the mouse.

The stonecutter said to the mouse, "Get into this when the cat comes. See how scared and angry that cat will get."

The next day the cat came back. The mouse got into the block and called, "Cat! You are too fat to have any lunch today."

The cat jumped at the mouse. But the mouse was safely protected by the clear stone wall, a wall the cat could not see.

The cat was so scared by the wall he could not see that he turned and ran.

The mouse and the stonecutter did not see that cat again. But they left the clear block by the door, just in case.

Books to Read

What Can You Make of It?
by Franz Brandenberg
A family of mice saves so many things it takes seven vans to move them to a new house. What will they do?

Dangerous Fish by Ray Broekel
Do you want to know which fish to watch out for in the water? This book has great pictures.

The Big Kite Contest
by Dorotha Ruthstrom
When Stephen's kite broke, he did not think he could get into the big kite contest. Find out how he did.

Picture Dictionary

Words That Name Animals

alligator   alligators
An alligator must live in a warm place.
When the land is cold, alligators go
into the warm water.

pack rat   pack rats
A pack rat is a good builder. Pack rats
save shiny things in their homes.

penguin   penguins
A penguin is a sea bird that does not
fly. Penguins use their wings for
swimming instead of for flying.

roadrunner   roadrunners
It's hard to take a picture of a
roadrunner. Roadrunners run too fast.

Words That Name Things

airplane   airplanes
An airplane is a flying machine.
Airplanes fly fast.

desert   deserts
A desert is a dry hot place.
Cactus plants grow in deserts.

machine   machines
A machine helps us do our work.
Machines are made of parts that
work together.

snowshoe   snowshoes
Snowshoes are big and flat.
People put snowshoes on their feet
to help them walk in deep snow.

Action Words

carry

Molly and Mike carry their books in
a backpack. They are carrying the
books to school.

count

Ted will count to ten. When he
is done counting, he will look
for the children.

hurt

The cat hurt its paw. It walked
slowly because its paw was hurting.

love

Lisa and John love to read.
They are loving their new book
about horses.

Ways to Use Words

bark   barks

Bark protects trees the way skin protects people.

The dog barks when people come to the door.

cross

Be careful when you cross the street.

Ann was cross when there was no cake left.

direction   directions

The teacher gave directions for doing the work.

The park is in this direction.

Ways to Use Words

land

The farmer grows vegetables on his land.

The airplane can land here.

note

Sue is writing a thank you note.

"Sing this note," said the teacher.

watch

Abe likes to watch fish at the Aquarium.

My watch is not working. I don't know what time it is.

Things I Need To Know

Do Not Litter
Keep places clean by not throwing things on the ground.

Entrance
The entrance sign shows the way to go into a building or a room.

Information
When you ask for information you may find out how, when, or where something will happen.

Restaurant
You can get good food at this restaurant.

Word List

The words below are listed by unit. Following each word is the page of first appearance of the word.

Unit 1, 7–17

pipe 9
break 9
fix 9
doctor 10
cried 10
paw 10
vet 10
sore 11
cage 12
fur 12
hug 12

Unit 2, 18–29

neighbor 19
street 19
safe 19
note 20
prize 20
welcome 22
surprise 22
kitten 24
reward 25

Unit 3, 30–40

busy 31
bedroom 32
messy 32
enjoy 32
yours 33
toy 32
cleaner 33
true 33

it's 34
woke 35
penguin 36

Unit 4, 41–53

view 43
tall 43
building 43
best 43
set 44
hill 44
who's 44
spout 45
over 45
pull 46
could 47
spy 48
floor 49
candle 50
bet 51

Unit 5, 54–63

off 55
carry 55
think 56
feet 56
land 56
there 56
him 57
quite 57
sad 58
full 58
probably 58
open 59

treat 59
were 60
waterway 60
heat 61
fed 61
steep 61
meat 62
seat 62

Unit 6, 64–74

mountain 65
ranch 65
radio 65
airplane 65
shed 66
sweep 67
rule 67
done 67
course 67
boots 68
took 68
dust 68
slowly 68
farther 69
those 69
sled 71
sway 71

Unit 7, 75–87

desert 77
home 77
dirt 77
dry 77
rat 78

dug 78
instead 78
cactus 79
again 79
low 79
food 80
roadrunner 80
mule 81
deer 81
ready 82
lemonade 84
bug 86
jug 86
rug 87

Unit 8, 88–100

large 89
such 89
perfect 89
almost 89
lion 90
may 91
glad 91
cross 92
grass 92
jeep 93
count 94
missing 94
trample 95
snap 95
snarl 93
crack 96
snack 97

222